W9-BSQ-457

Encyclopedia Brown's
Second Book of
Puzzles and Games

Encyclopedia Brown's
Second Book of Puzzles and Games

BY JIM RAZZI

Based upon the Encyclopedia Brown Series
created by Donald J. Sobol

A BANTAM SKYLARK BOOK

ENCYCLOPEDIA BROWN'S SECOND BOOK
OF PUZZLES AND GAMES
*A Bantam Skylark Book / published by arrangement with
Elsevier/Nelson Books*

Bantam Skylark edition / February 1980

All rights reserved.
Underlying material selected from The Encyclopedia
Brown series created by Donald J. Sobol.
Copyright © 1980 by Donald J. Sobol.

Puzzles, games and illustrations copyright
© 1980 by Bantam Books, Inc.
*This book may not be reproduced in whole or in part, by
mimeograph or any other means, without permission.
For information address: Bantam Books, Inc.*

ISBN 0-553-15059-6

Published simultaneously in the United States and Canada

---

*Bantam Books are published by Bantam Books, Inc. Its trade-
mark, consisting of the words "Bantam Books" and the por-
trayal of a bantam, is Registered in U.S. Patent and Trademark
Office and in other countries. Marca Registrada. Bantam
Books, Inc., 666 Fifth Avenue, New York, New York 10019.*

PRINTED IN THE UNITED STATES OF AMERICA

0 9 8 7 6 5 4 3 2 1

Introduction

Encyclopedia and the gang are back for more *Puzzles and Games* fun! Come along and once again match wits with America's favorite ten-year-old detective.

Here are more Spot the Clue cases plus cryptograms, picture puzzles, games, mazes and lots more. All you need to join the fun is a pencil. So go get one and start right in!

Fingerprint Maze

Encyclopedia Brown has found a fingerprint at the scene of the crime. He magnifies it to study it more clearly and then he discovers an *amazing* thing. The fingerprint is a maze!

See if you can find your way from START (arrow) to FINISH (star).

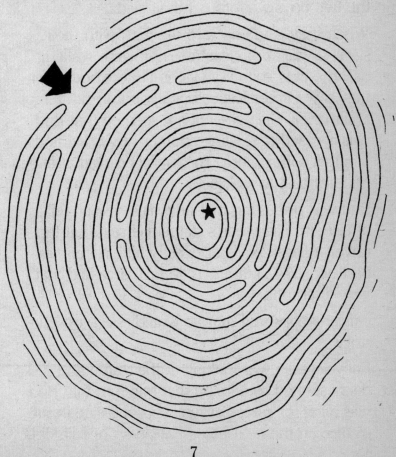

Spot the Clue

Encyclopedia and Buck Connors were walking along in the park in the snow. It had been snowing heavily for about an hour. All of a sudden, it stopped. Encyclopedia looked at his watch. It was exactly two o'clock. "We still have plenty of time to go sledding," he told Buck. Buck agreed and the two boys went to get their sleds.

When they came back to the park with their sleds, it was an hour later. They were walking past the new statue of General Sherwood when they saw Officer Kepps holding onto Bud Shulman, a Tiger member. It seemed that Bud was accused of stealing another boy's sled and hiding it somewhere. The theft occurred at fifteen minutes past two o'clock.

Bud was protesting that he was at the unveiling of General Sherwood's statue. He said that the unveiling took place at exactly fifteen minutes past two. The statue *was*, in fact, unveiled that very afternoon.

Officer Kepps said that he would check on Bud's story.

Encyclopedia was looking at the statue and suddenly spotted something that told him that Bud was lying for sure. Can you spot the clue in the picture on the next page that Encyclopedia did?

The One Glass Mystery

It was a slow-moving day at the Brown Detective Agency so Sally was keeping Encyclopedia's brain working by giving him a mystery to solve.

She took out four glasses and filled two of them with water. She then arranged them like this:

1   2   3   4

There were two full glasses and two empty glasses in a row.

"Now here's the mystery," said Sally. "How can you have a full glass, an empty glass, a full glass and an empty glass by moving only one glass in the row?"

Encyclopedia thought hard for a while and then he just smiled and did it. Can you?

Around the World

Encyclopedia Brown never goes too far from Idaville, but sometimes he dreams of visiting faraway places. Below are some of the places that Encyclopedia would like to go to. They are well-known cities and countries around the world. Just add a straight line to each letter to complete the names of them. The dots separate each letter.

| ·] · Λ · V · C · Λ

Λ · F · N · Y · C · P · ⻏

P ·] · N · C

Γ · Λ · Λ · Λ · V · Λ

S · Γ · Π · | · | · Λ · Λ · V

Γ · P · Λ · V · Γ · F

The Great Handball Game

Bugs Meany has challenged Encyclopedia Brown to a two-walled handball game for the championship of Idaville. Let's see who wins.

To play:

There are two ways to play: The solitaire version and the two-player version.

The solitaire version: You will play for both Bugs and Encyclopedia. Decide who goes first and then give them a turn each. Pick any line you want to on the PLAYER'S LINE. With a pencil, follow that line as it bounces off the walls and onto the SCORING LINE. Mark down the score (either zero or one) in the SCORING BOX next to the name of the player whose turn it was. After you've used a line, cross it out on the PLAYER'S LINE. Keep on taking turns for Bugs and Encyclopedia until all the lines are used. Whoever gets the highest score, wins.

Note: Do not follow a line with your eye before picking it. It won't be fun that way.

Two-player version: Put your own names in the SCORING BOX and then play the same as above. Take a turn each until all lines are used up.

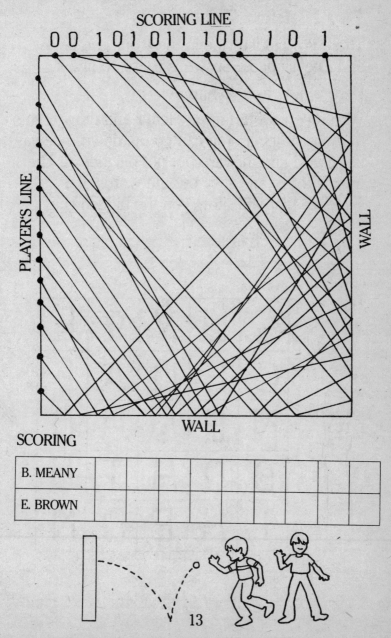

SCORING LINE

0 0 1 0 1 0 1 1 1 0 0 1 0 1

PLAYER'S LINE

WALL

WALL

SCORING

| B. MEANY | | | | | | | | | | |
| E. BROWN | | | | | | | | | | |

13

The Hidden Clue

There is a hidden clue in the word grid below and Encyclopedia Brown is trying to find it.

Here is how to help him out.

With a pencil, start at any letter and draw a line to the next letter. You can go up, down, sideways, backward and forward but not diagonally. The trick is to try and spell out the words of a sentence that will show you the <u>hidden clue.</u>

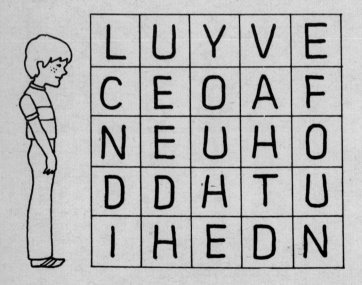

The Ransom Note

Someone has stolen Tubby Flander's bicycle and the bikenapper has left him a ransom note. The suspects are narrowed down to: Phil Bibbs, Flip Jenkins, Carl Updike and Mary Mumford. Encyclopedia Brown has tricked them into writing their names for him. He is now comparing their signatures with the handwriting on the note. Can you help him out and tell him who wrote the ransom note?

Here are the suspect's signatures:

Phil Bibbs   Carl Updike

Flip Jenkins   Mary Mumford

Here is the ransom note:

If you want your bike back, leave twenty dollars by the mailbox at first street and third avenue.

Circus Crossword

In *The Case of Merko's Grandson*, Grandpa turns out to be Grandma. In any case, she was The Great Merko, the greatest trapeze performer ever seen in the circus. See how well you can perform on this circus crossword. All you need for admission is a pencil.

ACROSS

2. Circus tents (2 wds.)
6. Famous circus (2 wds.)
7. I am
8. Daily paper
10. Circus house
12. Circus animal
13. Big cat sound
15. "...young man on the _ _ _ _ _ _ _ _ _ _ _ _ _"
17. From the Alps
20. Ringling Brothers
21. _ _ _ _ _ from a cannon

DOWN

1. It's raining _ _ _ _ & _ _ _ _
2. Circus marching groups
3. Circus long-leg
4. What circus lions are
5. Not nice
6. Number-calling game
9. Don't lose
11. _ _ _ _ _ _ – _ _ _ _ _ circus
12. Elephants' noses
13. Used to tie down tent
14. Funny circus people
16. Circus _ _ _ _ _ _, how it comes to town
18. Very cold water
19. Employ

16

Follow That Man!

Follow a suspect to his hideout just like Chief Brown would!

The map on the next page shows city blocks. The smaller boxes in the blocks represent stores. You are going to follow a suspect as he zigzags his way to his hideout, doing some shopping on the way.

Here's how to play:

Take a pencil and start at X (where you first spotted your man). Draw a pencil line, following directions below, showing the suspect's movements.

Directions:

He went *west* on 5th Ave., *north* on Hargrove Rd., *west* on 6th Ave., *south* on Olive Rd. to the second store he came to on the *west* side of the road. He continued *south*, then *east* on 3rd Ave., *south* on Hargrove Rd., *west* on 2nd Ave., *north* on Olive Rd. to the third store he came to on the *east* side of the road. He continued *north*, then *west* on 5th Ave., *south* on Main Rd., *west* on 4th Ave. to the second store he came to on the *north* side of the road. He continued *west*, then *south* on Market Rd., *east* on 3rd Ave. to the first store on the *northwest* corner of a block. Then he went *south* on Main Rd., *west* on 2nd Ave., *north* on Baker Rd., to the last store he came to on the *east* side of the road. This store was his hideout.

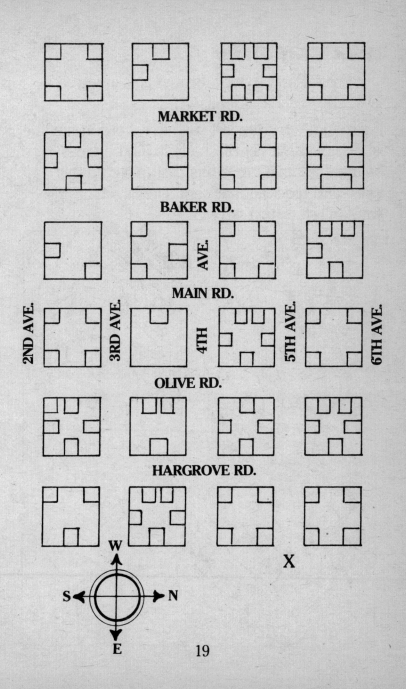

MARKET RD.

BAKER RD.

MAIN RD.

OLIVE RD.

HARGROVE RD.

2ND AVE.

3RD AVE.

4TH AVE.

5TH AVE.

6TH AVE.

X

W

S

N

E

19

Wild West Show

Out West, Encyclopedia Brown gets involved in
The Case of the Ambushed _ _ _ _ _ _.

Figure out what the last six-letter word in the title
is. Then, with a pencil, shade in all the areas
below that have the letters that make up that
word and see what happens. Here's a hint: "We
wouldn't steer you wrong!"

Rainy Day Trick

It was a rainy day and business was slow. To pass the time, Encyclopedia showed Sally Kimball his favorite card trick. It went like this: He showed Sally two stacks of cards on the gasoline can. He picked up one stack and told Sally to pick a card from it and not show it to him. When Sally did this, Encyclopedia took the card back, without looking at it, and placed it somewhere in the middle of the *other* stack. He then picked up that other stack, shuffled the cards, looked through them and picked out Sally's card immediately.

Sally loved the trick and asked Encyclopedia to show her how it was done.

Encyclopedia told her:

"It's the easiest trick in the world. First put all the red cards in one stack and all the black cards in another. Your audience shouldn't see you do this of course. Put the stacks on a table top and then call in your audience. Pick up a stack, either one, and have someone pick a card from it. Then simply put that card into the *other* stack. That card will be the only card in that stack that will be a different color. Shuffle the stack, then look through it privately for the different colored one. Show it to your audience when you find it. It's as simple as that!"

Strange Music

Encyclopedia Brown and his friends sometimes use musical codes to send secret messages. They make up their own letters for the actual letters of the notes.

Here's one that Encyclopedia has just made up. Look at the musical code key and then decode the message from Encyclopedia to his partner, Sally Kimball.

Musical Code Key

Secret Message Note: The vertical lines separate the words.

Decode message here

P. S. You can make up your own musical code to send secret messages yourself!

U.F.O.!

It's Idaville's first U.F.O. sighting! Encyclopedia Brown, Sally Kimball and a number of other kids all saw it. You see it too as you look up in the sky. The picture below is what you see flying over Idaville. Study the details and try to remember all you can. Then turn the page.

Draw the U.F.O.

The U.F.O. disappears and the excitement dies down a bit. Chief Brown, however, wants to ask the kids for a description of the U.F.O. He gives each one a sheet of blank paper and asks them to draw exactly what they saw. Your sheet of paper is below. Try to draw the U.F.O. you saw without looking back at it. When you are finished, turn back and see how close you came to the real thing.

Gem Word Find

In *The Case of the Diamond Necklace*, a mis-timed scream gave the game away. Encyclopedia sparkled as usual and solved the case quickly.

Now here's a gem of a word find. You can go forward, backward, vertically, horizontally, and diagonally. Draw a pencil line around each word as you find it.

Look for: DIAMONDS, OPAL, EMERALD, RUBY, SAPPHIRE, GARNET, JASPER, TOPAZ, TURQUOISE and PEARL.

```
J E R I H P P A S R A D J
G A R N I T E D R U B I A
T P S G A R N E T B Y A S
U O S P A O J M R B S M P
R Z P E M A L E U Y A O A
Q O P A L S P R B U P U R
U L I E Z S E A L R H N A
O D P E A R R L E L H D A
I S A J O R A D P O I S P
S T O P E Z L S O P R A E
E T U R Q U O I S A E P T
```

Spot the Clue

A phone call from Silas Pennyworth's male secretary brings Chief Brown and Encyclopedia to the millionaire's home. It looks like Mr. Pennyworth has been kidnapped! The secretary has found torn pieces of a note on the floor that seems to have been written by Mr. Pennyworth. Apparently they were left there as a clue by Mr. Pennyworth without the kidnappers noticing.

The secretary has left the pieces as he found them. Chief Brown does not want to move anything yet until he dusts for fingerprints. He does ask the secretary, however, if the signature on the note is Mr. Pennyworth's. The secretary says that it is. While his father is looking around, Encyclopedia studies the torn pieces on the floor. He reads the message by putting together the pieces in his mind. He then notices something that makes him realize that the note was never written by Silas Pennyworth!

Now, can you read the message on the next page *and* spot the clue that tipped Encyclopedia off?

house on
Drive.

am being
the old

call

Help! I
taken to

Maple
Please

Silas

Pennyworth

police!

27

Fish and Games!

Join Encyclopedia and his father as they go fishing. Here are two games to play while you're waiting for the fish to bite.

Strange Catch

Write in the three-letter words going down by following the clues. Read the middle row across and see what Encyclopedia and his father will never catch!

1. American Medical Association (initials)
2. Dogs are a favorite one
3. Upper limb
4. Short for umpire
5. "_ _ _ and eggs"
6. Inside a peach
7. Put 2 and 2 together.

1.	2.	3.	4.	5.	6.	7.

Tangled Lines

In the picture on the next page, you see Encyclopedia and his father with tangled lines. They got their own lines caught on some old ones that were in the water.

Here's how to play: Start at the WATER LINE and pick a line. Follow that line all the way down to see if you caught a fish or not. Take three chances only. If you catch three fish, you're great. Two, you're okay; one, you're so-so; none, stay home next time.

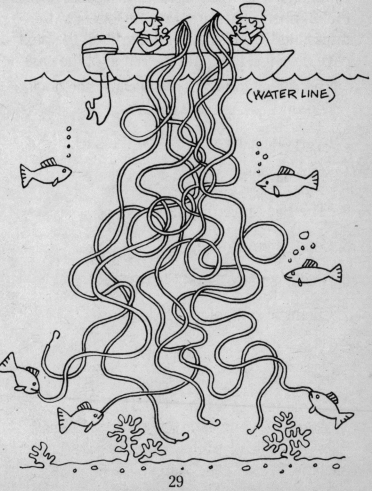

(WATER LINE)

Name the Case

A cold car helps Encyclopedia warm up and solve this cookie of a case. To find out which case it was, solve the acrostic puzzle that follows.

Here is what to do: Guess the words from the clues, and write the letters in the spaces above the numbers. Then transfer the letters to the same numbered boxes in the grid on the next page. You will then find the name of the case.

1. The car's hood was cold because the engine had no __ __ __ __ in it.

      2 3 14 10

2. Everyone likes a __ __ __ on the back.

      16 5 1

3. Not many: __ __ __

      9 22 23

4. "The Big Apple," initials: __ __ __

      18 17 4

5. Count them to sleep: __ __ __ __ __

      6 13 19 12 15

6. "Faith, __ __ __ __ and Charity"

      21 8 20 7

7. Chemical symbol for Hydrogen: __

      11

1	2	3	4	5	6	7	8	9	10	11	12
13	14	15	16	17	18	19	20	21	22	23	■

Crazy Graffiti

The latest thing in Idaville is crazy graffiti. The idea is to figure out what the words really stand for. It can be the name of an object or a common saying. For example, number 2 stands for Putdown.

Now see if you can figure out the rest.

1. CLASS

3. HAND

2. PUT

4. TALK
TALK

5. FRY

6. SHOT

7. HOLD

8. RAKEN

9. TOWN

10. TOWN

11. SHOULDER

12. SPOT

13. TIME

14. SNAKE

15. POT

16. HAND

17. SUN

18. NERVOUS BREAK

33

Encyclopedia Brown's Detective Tests

A lot of kids ask Encyclopedia if they have what it takes to be a good detective. Encyclopedia tells them that anyone who uses his eyes and brain can make a good detective. But for those of you who like to be tested, Encyclopedia has given you a few tests. See how well you can do.

Test #1

Draw a continuous line from house A to house B. You must go either vertically or horizontally only. The line must pass through every house, but only once. When you have finished, you must not have more than 21 straight lines in that one continuous line.

Test #2

There is something wrong with each picture below. Can you tell what it is?

1.

2.

3.

4.

5.

6.

Test #3

Try to get to the center of the maze without
making one mistake. You cannot check out a
path before you draw a line.

Test #4

In each row of drawings below, there is one that is different. Find the different one in each row and cross it out.

Row 1, Footprints

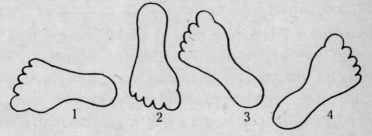

Row 2, Arrowheads

Row 3, Indian Bird Designs

Cryptograms

One of Encyclopedia Brown's favorite pastimes is solving cryptograms. A cryptogram is a code in which other letters are substituted for the real letters of the alphabet. Now, of course, in any one cryptogram, you don't know yet which letters stand for the real letters. You therefore have to figure it out a little at a time by trial and error. It's not as hard as it sounds. For instance, a single letter standing alone will usually stand for I or A. A group of three letters occurring frequently throughout the cryptogram will usually be AND or THE. These are used frequently in sentences. Two letters together will probably be AS, DO, IS, IT, OF, and so on.

As you start getting some letters, you will then get parts of words. Then you can guess what the rest of the letters are. For example: if you figured out G I O K I L stood for D O C T O ? so far, you can guess that the last L will stand for R and the word would be D O C T O R. Now of course you know that all the other L's in the cryptogram stand for R. You also know that all G's stand for D, all I's for O and so on.

Now let's start off on an easy one. The statement below, in cryptogram code, will tell you something about cryptograms. Decode the statement in the lines underneath. Since this is your first one, we will give you plenty of hints to start you off.

Here they are: Y=C, N=R, Q=U, O=S, C=G, U=Y, X=B, W=A, G=K.

Now here's the cryptogram

YNULPKCNWIO WNA BQJ EB

UKQ PWGA PDA PEIA WJZ

PDA PNKQXHA PK ZK PDAI

After you've solved this one, turn the page for more.

Surprise Nursery Rhyme

Here's a cryptogram of an old nursery rhyme with a surprise ending to it that is not in the original. Solve the cryptogram and you'll see what it is.

Here's some hints: A=H, N=U, R=Y, M=T, F=M, U=B, V=C

ANFIMR   WNFIMR   LTM   HG   T

— — — — — —   — — — — — —   — — —   — —   —

PTEE,

— — — — ,

ANFIMR   WNFIMR   ATW   T

— — — — — —   — — — — — —   — — —   —

ZKXTM   YTEE,

— — — — —   — — — — ,

UNM   AX   WBWG'M   UKXTD,   AX

— — —   — —   — — — — — —   — — — — — ,   — —

WBWG'M   VKTVD,

— — — — — —   — — — — — ,

AX   PTL   LH   ATKW-UHBEXW,

— —   — — —   — —   — — — — — — — — — — ,

AX   CNLM   UHNGVXW   UTVD!

— —   — — — —   — — — — — — —   — — — — !

Patriotic Song

This cryptogram is a famous old patriotic song. We've changed the last two lines, however, so don't go too fast. Here's the only hint we'll give you. It's about someone riding into town on his horse.

MOBYSS RCCRZS QOAS HC

‾ ‾ ‾ ‾ ‾ ‾   ‾ ‾ ‾ ‾ ‾ ‾   ‾ ‾ ‾ ‾   ‾ ‾

HCKB

‾ ‾ ‾ ‾

O-FWRWBU CB O DCBM,

‾ ‾ ‾ ‾ ‾ ‾ ‾   ‾ ‾   ‾   ‾ ‾ ‾ ‾ ‾,

GHIQY O GOBRKWQV WB

‾ ‾ ‾ ‾ ‾   ‾   ‾ ‾ ‾ ‾ ‾ ‾ ‾ ‾   ‾ ‾

VWG DCQYSH

‾ ‾ ‾   ‾ ‾ ‾ ‾ ‾ ‾

AORS CT QCZR POZCBSM

‾ ‾ ‾ ‾   ‾ ‾   ‾ ‾ ‾ ‾   ‾ ‾ ‾ ‾ ‾ ‾

Chilly Rebuses

One of Encyclopedia's cases involved a famous arctic explorer. It was a cold trail until Encyclopedia warmed up to the task and solved the mystery.

The answers to the rebuses that follow will be things found in cold places like the North and South Poles. Keep cool and you can solve them easily.

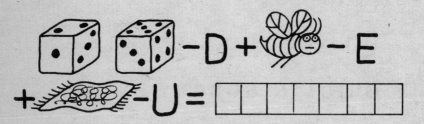

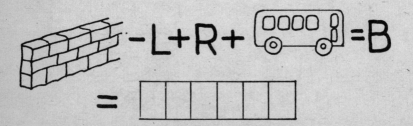

-W + ⚾ -BL = □□□□

E + 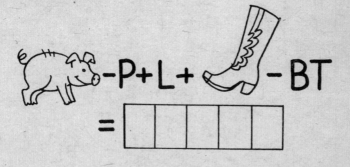 + 🌙 -ON = □□□□□□

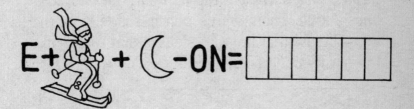 -P+L+ -BT
= □□□□□

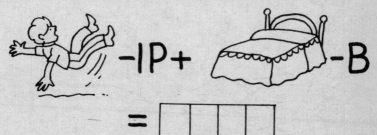 -IP+ -B
= □□□□

Pirates!

Encyclopedia and the gang are looking at some books about pirates. They learn that a pirate's flag is called a J_ _ _Y R_ _ _R.

If you figured out how to spell the name of a pirate's flag, complete the name in the dashed lines above. Then, with a pencil, shade in all the areas below that have the letters that make up the name. Can you see the J_ _ _Y R_ _ _R?

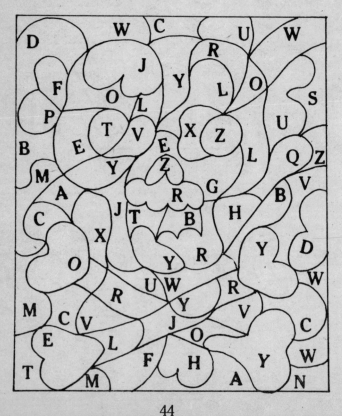

Baseball Word Find

In *The Case of the Secret Pitch*, a wrong date told Encyclopedia that a superstar baseball player never signed a check.

Baseball, however, will never go out of date. Take your turn at bat and see how you score on this baseball word find. You can go forward, backward, vertically, horizontally, and diagonally. Draw a pencil line around each word as you find it. Look for: BASEBALL, BAT, GLOVE, OUTFIELD, SHORTSTOP, CATCHER, PITCHER, HOMER, RUN, SCORES, COACH, and FOUL.

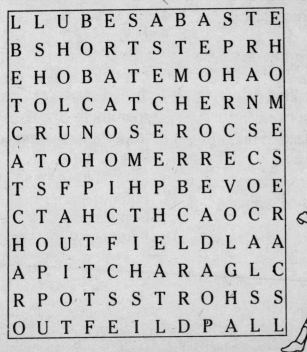

```
L L U B E S A B A S T E
B S H O R T S T E P R H
E H O B A T E M O H A O
T O L C A T C H E R N M
C R U N O S E R O C S E
A T O H O M E R R E C S
T S F P I H P B E V O E
C T A H C T H C A O C R
H O U T F I E L D L A A
A P I T C H A R A G L C
R P O T S S T R O H S S
O U T F E I L D P A L L
```

Dinosaur Crossword

Encyclopedia Brown once solved a case that involved cave paintings of dinosaurs. The paintings turned out to be fake, but dinosaurs really did exist at one time. Let's go back to that time and see if you can solve this crossword before a million years pass.

ACROSS

5. Puppy bark
7. Tyrannosaurus ＿ ＿ ＿
8. The two King Kongs
10. Not an old animal
12. Brother and
＿ ＿ ＿ ＿ ＿ ＿
13. Half a toy on a string
15. Indian house
16. School vehicle
19. Prehistoric human
20. Every
21. No caveman weapon
22. Unusual, valuable

DOWN

1. Large dinosaur
2. Stegosaurus & tricerotops
3. Mad
4. Caveman tools
5. Millions of
＿ ＿ ＿ ＿ ＿ ago
6. Cave decoration
9. Today's tusked mammoth
11. Important caveman invention
14. Musical instrument
17. Follows a scab (sometimes)
18. Finished; above

Spot the Clue

"There are a lot of phony beggars around lately," said Chief Brown as he sat at the dinner table.

It seemed that there were a gang of cheats going around town. They pretended to be lame or blind and were standing on corners asking people for money.

Encyclopedia wanted to hear more but he had a date with Sally Kimball to go to the movies. When he and Sally got off the bus downtown, they had to walk two blocks to the movie theater. On the way, they saw a blind man with a tin cup.

"Oh the poor man!" said Sally, as she reached into her jeans to get some money out. Encyclopedia was also about to give the blind man some money when he noticed something.

"Save your money!" he said. "That man's not blind!" Sally asked Encyclopedia how he knew. Encyclopedia told her. Can you spot the clue in the picture on the next page that Encyclopedia did?

Haunted Word Maze

Encyclopedia once had a case with a haunted client. But the ghost turned out to be a very alive thief who spirited away an expensive camera.

If the spirit moves *you,* try to do this haunted word maze. You must find words by drawing a continuous line from letter to letter until you spell the word. For example, we have found MUMMY for you. You can go forward, backward, horizontally, vertically and diagonally. However, you cannot jump over any letter. Starting anywhere you want to, find: GHOUL, BATS, GROANS, SCREAMS, WITCHES, WEREWOLVES, VAMPIRE and GHOST.

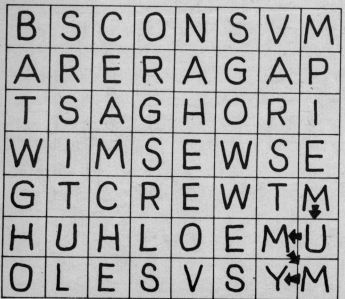

A Detective's Memory

To be a good detective like Encyclopedia Brown, you have to have a good memory. Play this memory game and see how good yours is.

First, study the sixteen items below for as long as you think necessary to memorize them. Then turn the page and list the items from memory. Don't peek back!

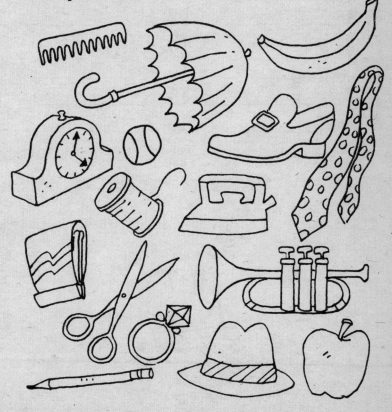

Memory Test

We will help jog your memory by putting the first letter of each object below. You fill in the rest.

1. C _____   9. B _____
2. U _____   10. S _____
3. B _____   11. M _____
4. S _____   12. H _____
5. T _____   13. T _____
6. C _____   14. P _____
7. T _____   15. R _____
8. I _____   16. A _____

24-Karat Puzzle

In *The Case of the Divining Rod,* Encyclopedia proves that all that glitters is not gold. He exposes a cheat trying to sell gold-finding rods to the kids of Idaville.

Now let's see if you can find some gold in the word game below. All you have to do is turn BASE GOLD into the real 24-karat stuff! Do it by changing the word BASE into GOLD. You have to do it in 4 steps by changing one letter at a time in each step to form a new word. Good luck!

BASE

1. _ _ _ _
2. _ _ _ _
3. _ _ _ _
4. _ _ _ _

Junk Sculpture Maze

In *The Case of the Junk Sculptor*, Encyclopedia
finds that a cold seat is a hot clue to solve the
case. See if you can solve this junk sculpture
maze. Start at the ARROW and find your way to
the STAR. You cannot cross a line.

Answers

Fingerprint Maze, page 7

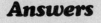

Spot the Clue, page 8

Encyclopedia noticed that the statue had some snow over all of it. Since he knew that it had stopped snowing at two o'clock, he realized that the unveiling must have been before two. If the unveiling had taken place at fifteen minutes past two, as Bud Shulman said, the statue would be clear of snow.

The One Glass Mystery, page 10

Just take Glass #2 and pour all the water into Glass #3. Then replace Glass #2. You only moved one glass! (This is a good one to try out on your friends.)

Around the World, page 11

L·O·N·D·O·N
N·E·W· Y·O·R·K
R·O·M·E
C·A·N·A·D·A
S·C·O·T·L·A·N·D
F·R·A·N·C·E

Answers

The Hidden Clue, page 14

L	U	Y	V	E
C	E	O	A	F
N	E	U	H	O
D	D	H	T	U
I	H	E	D	N

The Ransom Note, page 15

Phil Bibbs wrote the note.

Circus Crossword, pages 16 & 17

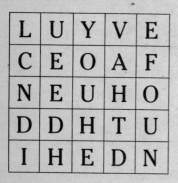

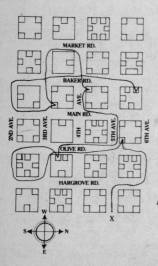

Follow That Man!, page 18

Answers

Wild West Show, page 20

The Case of the Ambushed *Cowboy*

Strange Music, page 22

The message reads: MEET ME ON SOUTH STREET AT TEN

Gem Word Find, page 25

Answers

Spot the Clue, page 26
The note reads:

After reading the note, Encyclopedia noticed that Silas Pennyworth's signature was different from the other writing. This was the clue that told him that Mr. Pennyworth didn't write the note. Remember, the secretary had said that it *was* Silas Pennyworth's signature. When shown this fact, the secretary became nervous and Chief Brown became suspicious. After hard questioning, the secretary admitted that he was part of the kidnap plot. He had written the note himself to throw the police off the track. They had then forced Mr. Pennyworth to sign it. Needless to say, the whole gang was caught and Mr. Pennyworth was rescued when the secretary led the police to the real hideout.

Fish and Games! page 28

A	P	A	U	H	P	A
M	E	R	M	A	I	D
A	T	M	P	M	T	D

Answers

Name the Case, page 30

1. HEAT 2. PAT 3. FEW 4. NYC 5. SHEEP 6. HOPE 7. H

T	H	E	C	A	S	E	O	F	T	H	E
H	A	P	P	Y	N	E	P	H	E	W	■

Crazy Graffiti, page 32

1. High Class 3. Handshake 4. Double talk 5. Small fry 6. Big shot 7. Hold up 8. Half-baked 9. Downtown 10. Uptown 11. Cold shoulder 12. Tight spot 13. Small time 14. Snake in the grass 15. Melting pot 16. Upper hand 17. Sunshine 18. Nervous breakdown

Answers

Encyclopedia Brown's Detective Tests, pages 34, 35, 36 & 37

Test #1

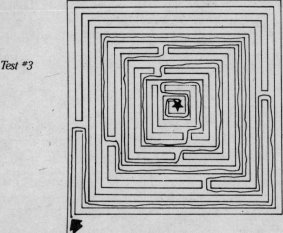

Test #2

1. The lamp is lit but not plugged in.
2. The television's screen is perfectly square. In reality it is not.
3. The cutting edges of the scissors are facing the wrong way.
4. The tree's shadow should be in the opposite direction.
5. An electric car does not give off exhaust.
6. The high-heeled boots would form different footprints in the snow.

Test #3

Test #4

Row 1, Footprints: number 3 is different
Row 2, Arrowheads: number 4 is different
Row 3, Indian Bird Design: number 3 is different

60

Answers

Cryptograms, pages 38, 39, 40 & 41

CRYPTOGRAMS ARE FUN IF
YOU TAKE THE TIME AND
THE TROUBLE TO DO THEM

HUMPTY DUMPTY SAT ON A
WALL,
HUMPTY DUMPTY HAD A
GREAT FALL,
BUT HE DIDN'T BREAK, HE
DIDN'T CRACK,
HE WAS SO HARD-BOILED,
HE JUST BOUNCED BACK!

YANKEE DOODLE CAME TO
TOWN
A-RIDING ON A PONY,
STUCK A SANDWICH IN
HIS POCKET
MADE OF COLD BALONEY

Spot the Clue, page 48

Encyclopedia noticed that the man had a newspaper in his pocket. A blind person would have no need of a newspaper. Encyclopedia therefore concluded that the blind man was part of that gang of phony beggars that his father had been talking about.

Answers

Chilly Rebuses, page 42

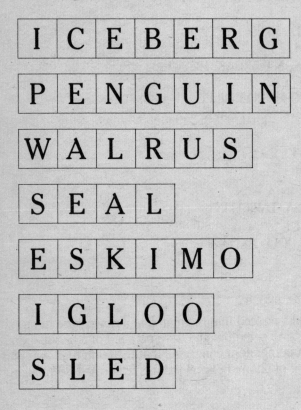

ICEBERG

PENGUIN

WALRUS

SEAL

ESKIMO

IGLOO

SLED

Answers

Pirates!, page 44

<u>JOLLY</u> <u>ROGER</u>

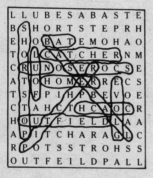

Baseball Word Find, page 45

Dinosaur Crossword, pages 46 & 47

Answers

Haunted Word Maze,
page 50

B	S →C	O	N →S	V	M
A	R →E	R	A	G	A	P
T →S	A	G	H →O	R ←I
W →I	M →S	E ←W	S	E
G	T →C	R →E →W	T	M
H	U	H	L ←O	E	M	U
O	L	E →S	V	S	Y	M

24-Karat Puzzle, page 53

  B A S E
1. B A <u>L</u> E
2. B A L <u>D</u>
3. B <u>O</u> L D
4. <u>G</u> O L D

Junk Sculpture Maze, page 54

If you have enjoyed this book, look for the other
Puzzles and Games *books at your favorite*
bookstore.

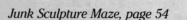